CHIMA IN PE...

Chima is on the verge of a catastrophe! A sinister black cloud has shrouded the floating Mount Cavora and the CHI-filled waterfalls have dried up. The natural balance has been disturbed and the tribes of Chima are suffering from the lack of their main energy source. Complete the picture with the correct stickers.

TO SAVE CHIMA

Facing a new threat, the tribes of Chima stopped fighting for CHI. Instead, they decided to work together for the sake of Chima. A "hero team" made of the best warriors from each tribe went to the Outlands to find the Legend Beasts – the mythical creatures that have the power to restart the CHI waterfalls and save Chima. Place the correct stickers next to the descriptions and meet the heroes.

LAVAL

The future ruler of the Lion Tribe. He still loves fun and adventures, but today, more than ever, he values Chima's law and traditions.

CRAGGER

The ruler of the Crocodiles wants to save Chima and find his father, King Crominus. This adventure might help restore his friendship with Laval, too.

The hero team would not be the same without Eris. This wise Eagle gives invaluable support to her friends. And she's a great fighter too.

ERIS

WORRIZ

The Wolves care only for themselves, but Worriz knows Chima needs their help too. He can be trusted during this mission . . . but not a day longer.

Mighty Gorzan is always relaxed. He seems more concerned with flowers and meditation, but his strength may be needed during this quest.

GORZAN

The Rhinos are incredibly strong and incredibly stupid. Rogon is no different, but in certain circumstances he has flashes of amazing intelligence.

ROGON

Razar takes every chance to make a profit. However, he puts aside his greed for while to help the others for the sake of Chima.

RAZAR

Bladvic is strong and very clever. This Bear can be a great asset to the team as long as he is awake. This problem is that he takes a nap whenever he can.

BLADVIC

PREDATORY MAZE

The Outlands are a very dangerous territory. Some carnivorous plants attacked Eris! Luckily Gorzan and Laval arrived to help her. Guide the three heroes out of the predatory maze and place the stickers with their portraits at the bottom of the page.

SURPRISE!

Quite unexpectedly another warrior joined the team – a female Rhino – to keep an eye on Rogon and make sure he was safe. Follow the lines and put the letters in the correct boxes to find the name of the clever Rhino and complete the picture with the correct sticker.

SPIDERS ATTACK!

The Predatory Plants were not the only danger that awaited the travellers in the Outlands. A group of fierce Spider warriors suddenly attacked the team. Find two identical Spider warriors in the picture and circle them.

SURROUNDED

The army of evil Spiders surrounded Laval and his warriors. Eris and Razar flew up to look for the way out. Help the birds follow the path through the labyrinth by stepping only on the stones where the number is increased by 2. Mark the path with arrow stickers for the other heroes to follow.

START ▽

7	6	1	8	9	4	9	3	9	1
6	8	10	17	12	14	16	19	20	21
13	9	12	9	10	67	18	23	25	29
7	7	14	16	18	20	22	22	24	26
29	4	4	8	4	3	24	9	10	11

▽ FINISH

EVIL WARRIORS

For hundreds of years nobody knew if there were any inhabitants in the Outlands other than the Legend Beasts. It turned out that the Outlands Tribes were not only hostile but greedy too – they were responsible for blocking up the CHI waterfalls of Mount Cavora! Place the stickers matching the shadows and read about the evil warriors from the Outlands.

The sting on the tip of the King Scorpion's tail contains venom that enables him to control a victim for a short time. But this Scorpion wants all the CHI so he can control the world!

SCORM

The Spider Queen looks revolting to every creature except for the Spiders, who find her impossibly alluring. The hideous and vain Spinlyn believes CHI makes her even more beautiful.

SPINLYN

8-9

10

12

15

13

14

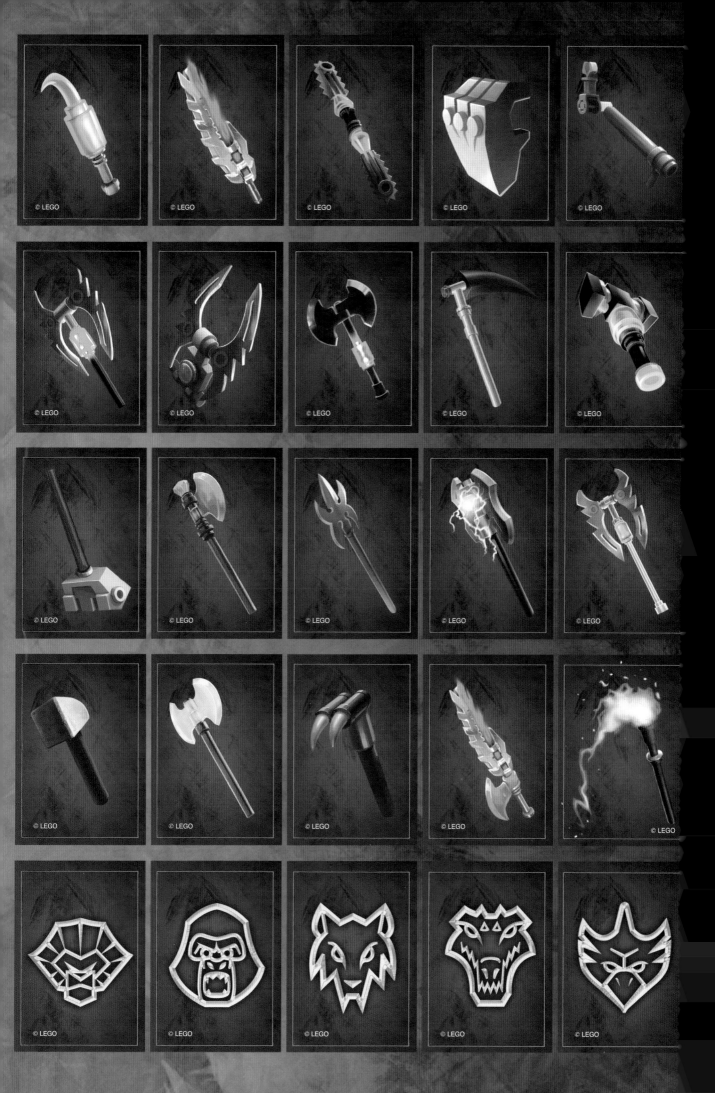

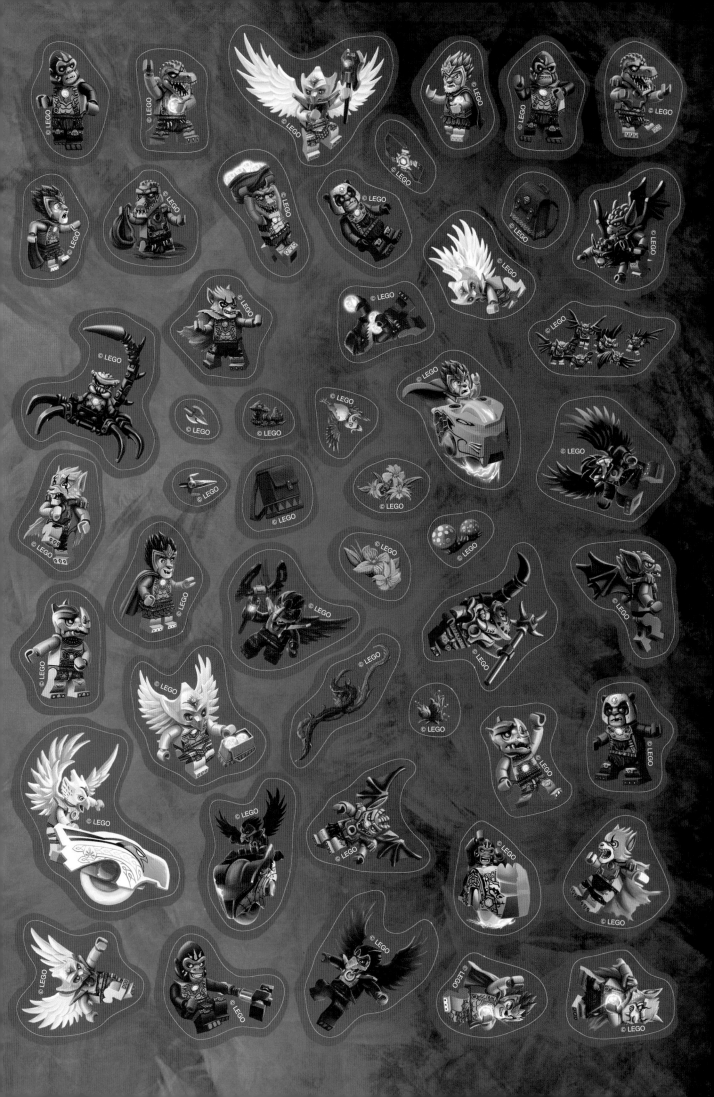

BLISTA

He's one of the best warriors from the Bat Tribe, but Blista would rather be playing tricks than fighting. After all, creating the black cloud around Mount Cavora with the other Bats was the best trick of all!

SCUTTER

He may not be the smartest Scorpion, but Scutter is very strong. His combat style is simple – ram an opponent with his massive body and jab them quickly with the venomous sting at the end of his tail. Ouch!

Sparacon is an exceptionally cold, methodical, and relentless Spider soldier. You can never tell what he's thinking, but his thoughts are never warm. He's amazingly inventive, especially when it comes to using the four spider legs on his back in battle . . .

SPARACON

During a scouting mission Eris discovered that the Legend Beasts had been captured by the Outlands tribes! In preparation for the rescue, the friends are checking their weapons. Each row below should have the same set of weapons.

Complete the sets with the correct weapon stickers.

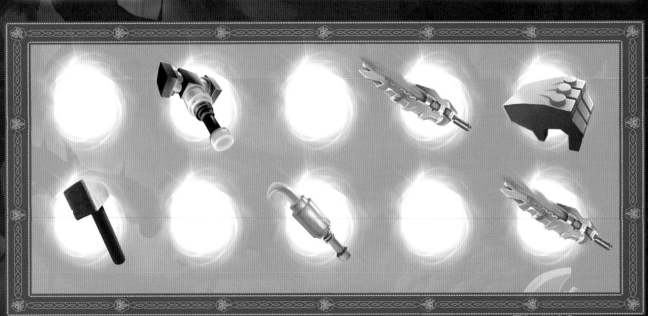

The Scorpions, Spiders and Bats want to conquer Chima and they are not going to let the Legend Beasts go without a fight. There are five differences between these two pictures. How fast can you spot all of them?

A NEW ALLY

Years ago a young Lion warrior named Lavertus had to leave his tribe for mysterious reasons. He settled in the Outlands, where he built a mini-fortress and filled it with his amazing inventions. Now he's helping Laval's team. Complete the battle scene with the stickers of Gorzan and Cragger then find their new ally's name in the grid.

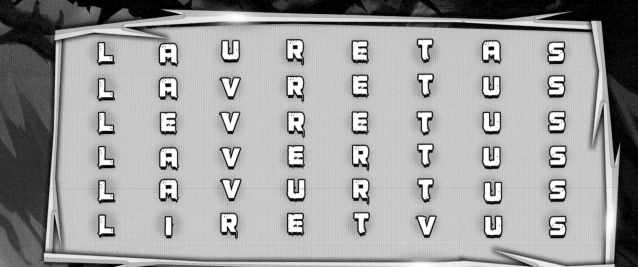

L	A	U	R	E	T	A	S
L	A	V	R	E	T	U	S
L	E	V	R	E	T	U	S
L	A	V	E	R	T	U	S
L	A	V	U	R	T	U	S
L	I	R	E	T	V	U	S

Thanks to his knowledge of the Outlands, his unique inventions, skills and experience, Lavertus became an ally whom Laval's team could only dream of.

Use the correct stickers to complete this sudoku game. Remember, the characters may not appear twice in any row or column.

BAT CAVE

Laval and Eris arrived at the cave of the Bat Tribe to free the Legend Beasts imprisoned there. They must follow the clues given to them by Lavertus so they're not spotted by the enemy. Use the Lavertus stickers to mark their path across the rocks.

CLUES: 2 steps right, 3 steps down, 1 step left, 2 steps down, 2 steps right

START

FINISH

After many battles, Laval and his friends finally managed to set the Legend Beasts free! If the legends are true, the beasts will be able to bring balance back to Chima. But . . . that's another story.

Place stickers with symbols of the tribes represented by the Legend Beasts shown in the picture below.

ANSWERS

Page 4. PREDATORY MAZE

Page 5. SURPRISE!

R I N O N A

Page 6. SPIDERS ATTACK!

Page 7. SURROUNDED

7	6	1	8	9	4	9	3	9	1
6	8	10	17	12	14	15	19	20	21
13	9	12	9	10	67	18	23	25	29
7	7	14	16	19	20	22	22	24	26
29	4	4	8	4	3	24	9	10	11

Page 10. WEAPON CHECK

Page 11. THE OUTLANDS TRIBES

Page 12. A NEW ALLY

L	A	U	R	E	T	A	S
L	A	V	R	E	T	T	S
L	A	E	V	R	E	U	S
L	M	V	E	R	T	T	S
L	A	V	U	R	T	U	S
L	I	R	E	T	V	U	S

Page. 14 BAT CAVE

Page 13. LION IN EXILE

16